Seerah Stories Out Loud!

Scan this QR code on your smartphone or tablet for a free audio reading of "Ka'b's Big Decision"

Need help?
Visit www.education-enriched.co.uk/audiobooks

~ For my children ~
R S KHAN

"Ka'b's Big Decision" is the second in a series of tales from the lives of the Companions. The series is aimed at inspiring Muslim children and instilling love in their hearts for those who were closest to the Messenger of Allah (may Allah's peace and blessings be upon him).

The reference for the events in this book are based upon the narrations found in the collections of hadith including that of *Saheeh ul Bukhari* within which Ka'b's story is narrated through his son.

Disclaimer: The illustrations contained in this storybook are not intended to be accurate depictions of the Companions (may Allah be pleased with them). Additionally, efforts have been made to make it clear that the Prophet (may Allah's peace and blessings be upon him) has not been depicted in any form.

First published in 2016 by Education Enriched
www.education-enriched.co.uk

ISBN: 978-0-9930436-3-5

Printed in Croatia

Ka'b's Big Decision

Written by R S Khan

Illustrated by H Chinthaka

PUBLISHED BY EDUCATION ENRICHED

Have you heard, have you heard, the story of Ka'b,

A young man who made a mistake?

Let me tell you his tale from beginning to end,

What a journey we're going to take!

It started one day when the Muslims were told

To get ready for an expedition,

They would journey afar in the fierce, fiery heat,

What a dangerous, difficult mission!

Some were allowed to stay in Madinah,

Like the weak, the poor and the sick,

But everyone else had to go to Tabook,

Like young Ka'b, who was strong and quite rich!

When the time came for the Muslims to leave,

Where was Ka'b? Where was Ka'b? Was he there?

No! He was lingering, back in his house,

It was clear he was going nowhere!

As soon as Ka'b realised he'd been left behind,

His heart must have sunk like a stone.

He had left it too late to catch up with the group,

So now he was all on his own!

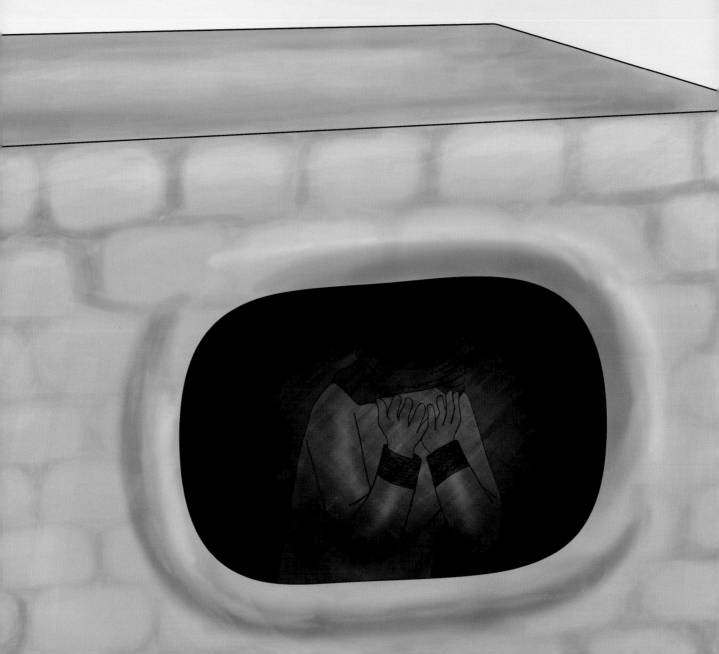

So how was Ka'b feeling? Oh, how was Ka'b feeling

At home, while the others were out?

He was feeling so terribly worried and sad,

That his bad deed would soon be found out!

Meanwhile, the others were on their way back,

To their wonderful, welcoming homes.

They had journeyed afar in the fierce, fiery heat,

And had not even grumbled or groaned!

The trek had been hard, the trek had been harsh,

The trek had been terribly long,

Yet the prize from Allah would be worth it, of course,

Oh how Ka'b wished that he too had gone!

The Prophet (upon him be peace) arrived home,

And asked Ka'b why he'd not come along.

Ka'b thought he could lie to get out of the mess,

But knew lying would be one more wrong!

So Ka'b then decided to tell him the truth,

"I have no excuse," he replied.

He knew his Creator could see all his deeds,

There was nowhere for young Ka'b to hide!

Ka'b had been brave and had spoken the truth,

He must have felt frightened inside.

But would this make up for his mighty mistake?

It was up to Allah to decide!

The Muslims were told not to speak to young Ka'b,

Until Allah made His decision.

Ka'b knew that Allah was Most-Just and Most-Kind,

So he prayed that he would be forgiven.

But then came a man with a message for Ka'b

From a king who had written a letter,

Inviting young Ka'b to move to his land,

Where the king said he'd treat him much better.

But Ka'b knew that this was a test from Allah,

So he threw the king's letter away.

By the Prophet (upon him be peace) would he wait,

Young Ka'b's love for Allah made him stay.

After fifty long days, Ka'b had heard no good news,

He felt gloomy and terribly glum,

He sat on the roof after finishing prayer,

Feeling sorry for what he had done.

All of a sudden, young Ka'b heard a man,

Calling out at the top of his voice.

He had climbed up a hill and had started to shout,

"Oh Ka'b, son of Malik, REJOICE!"

Allah the Almighty had sent the good news,

In a verse He revealed on that day,

That He had forgiven young Ka'b's big mistake,

And had washed his bad deed right away!

Joyfully, Ka'b put his head on the ground,

And bowed down to the One who sees all.

He knew he should thank his compassionate Lord,

Who'd forgiven his deed after all.

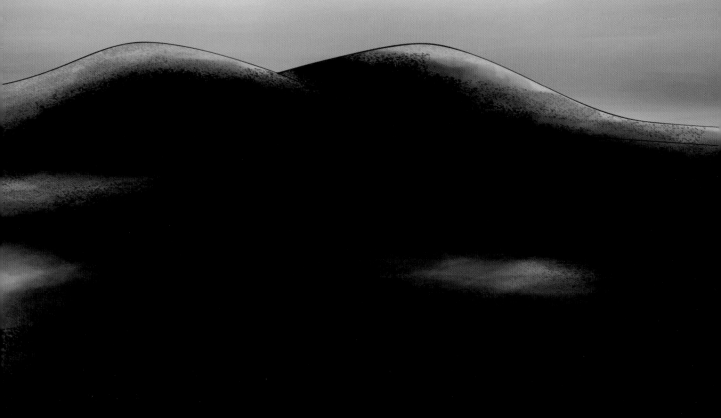

After hearing the news, many Muslims went out,

It was Ka'b whom they wanted to meet.

One man came hurrying, riding a horse,

Another ran fast on his feet.

Ka'b soon decided to go to the mosque,

To meet with the best of all men,

"Assalamu 'alaykum," Ka'b happily said,

Overjoyed to be with him again!

The Prophet (upon him be peace) then replied,

His face glowed with joy and delight,

"Be happy, this is the best day of your life!"

Everything had at last been put right.

Ka'b gave some charity from his own wealth,

To thank his Creator once more.

He wanted to make Allah happy with him,

By giving his wealth to the poor.

May Allah be pleased with this brave, honest man,

Who made up for his big mistake,

By telling the truth, though he'd get into trouble,

Just for Allah, His Lord's, sake!

What a perfect example Ka'b gave you and me,

Let us thank Allah, the Most High,

What a perfect example Ka'b gave you and me,

So to be brave like Ka'b, let us try!

"And [He also forgave] the three who were left behind [and regretted their error] to the point that the earth closed in on them in spite of its vastness and their souls confined them and they were certain that there is no refuge from Allah except in Him. Then He turned to them so they could repent. Indeed, Allah is the Accepting of repentance, the Merciful."

(Surah at-Tawbah 9:118)

This is the verse that was revealed about Ka'b ibn Malik and the other two who remained behind, informing them of Allah's forgiveness (may Allah be pleased with them all).